AMAZING SOLOS
for cello and keyboard

selected and arranged by Howard Harrison

London · New York · Berlin · Sydney

Composer's Note

The music in this book is appealing, sometimes truly great music which just happens to be simple. None of the pieces is merely 'educational' – almost all of them had successful lives of their own before they found their way here – and they have all been chosen for their individual, purely musical strengths. However, the book is more than just a collection of performable pieces; the pieces in it are roughly graded and very varied in their demands, so that any player who works through them will have the chance to consolidate and polish their technique. They are also more than usually varied in style, so I hope they will give some unexpected pleasures and signpost some interesting and enjoyable pathways that might otherwise have remained unexplored.

Anmerkung des Komponisten

Die Stücke in diesem Band, von denen einige besonders bedeutsam sind, sind äußerst ansprechend und gleichzeitig auch einfach. Es sind keine typischen Unterrichtsstücke – die meisten waren durchaus erfolgreich, bevor sie, aufgrund ihrer individuellen, rein musikalischen Stärken in diesem Band aufgenommen wurden. Es handelt sich dabei jedoch nicht nur um eine Sammlung aufführbarer Stücke, sondern um solche, die dem Spieler aufgrund ihrer Stufungen und vielseitigen Anforderungen die Möglichkeit zum Konsolidieren und Ausfeilen ihrer Fähigkeit geben. Auch stilmäßig sind sie von besonderer Vielseitigkeit und ich hoffe, daß sie nicht nur eine Quelle der Freude, sondern auch ein Wegweiser zu neuen, bisher unerforschten Pfaden sein werden.

Note du Compositeur

Les musiques de ce recueil pour si attirantes qu'elles soient – et même parfois importantes – n'en sont pas moins d'une grande simplicité. Il n'est pas de morceau qui ne soit qu'éducationnel, presque tous ont eu une carrière réussie avant de se retrouver groupés. De plus leur choix fut dicté par leurs caractères individuels, purement musicaux. L'ensemble est toutefois bien davantage qu'une simple collection de morceaux jouables: gradués de façon approximative, ils requièrent de la part des exécutants des talents divers, tant et si bien que la technique de ceux qui les joueront tous s'en trouvera consolidée et perfectionnée. La variété de leurs styles permettra donc, du moins je l'espère, qu'ils soient source de plaisirs inattendus autant qu'indicateurs de voies intéressantes qui, sans eux, seraient restées sans explorateurs.

作曲家の言葉

　本作品集には魅力的で、時には本当に偉大な名曲でありながらも、演奏が簡単な曲ばかりを集めました。単なる「教材」は一曲もありません。ほとんど全てが、ここに選ばれる前に既に有名になった曲です。そして全て、独立した、純粋に音楽的な要素を前提に選ばれたものです。しかし、単なる曲集でもありません。各曲は大まかに段階が付けられ、それぞれ様々な要素を必要としますから、演奏することによってテクニックを磨き、確実なものとすることができるのです。また、一般の作品集よりも様々なスタイルを取り混ぜていますから、思ってもいなかった喜びを体験され、そうでなければ経験することのなかったような、面白く、楽しい道を発見する手がかりとなればと願っています。

CONTENTS · INHALT · TABLE DE MATIERES

Bliss

Franz Schubert

Woogie Boogie

Howard Harrison

Chorale

from the St. Matthew Passion

Johann Sebastian Bach

Tanz des Burgermeisters
(Mayor's Dance)

Michael Praetorius

Byker Hill

English traditional

D. C. al Coda

CODA   a tempo

Lovely Joan

English traditional

Scherzando

from For Children

Béla Bartók

Pleasantry II
from For Children

Béla Bartók

Allegro

Wolfgang Amadeus Mozart

Troika
from Lieutenant Kijé

Serge Prokofieff

Lord Inchiquin

Turlough Carolan

Tambourin I

Jacques Aubert

attacca Tambourin II ad lib.

Tambourin II

Jacques Aubert

Mayim, Mayim

Israeli traditional

The House of the Rising Sun

American traditional

Stars, No Moon

Peruvian traditional

Paragon Rag

Scott Joplin

Three Moravian Folk Songs

1. Budíček
(Morning Call)

Leoš Janáček

2. Psaníčko
(Little Letter)

Leoš Janáček

3. Stalost
(Constancy)

Leoš Janáček

Maria
from West Side Story

Leonard Bernstein

The Blue Beyond

Howard Harrison

Larghetto

Antonio Vivaldi

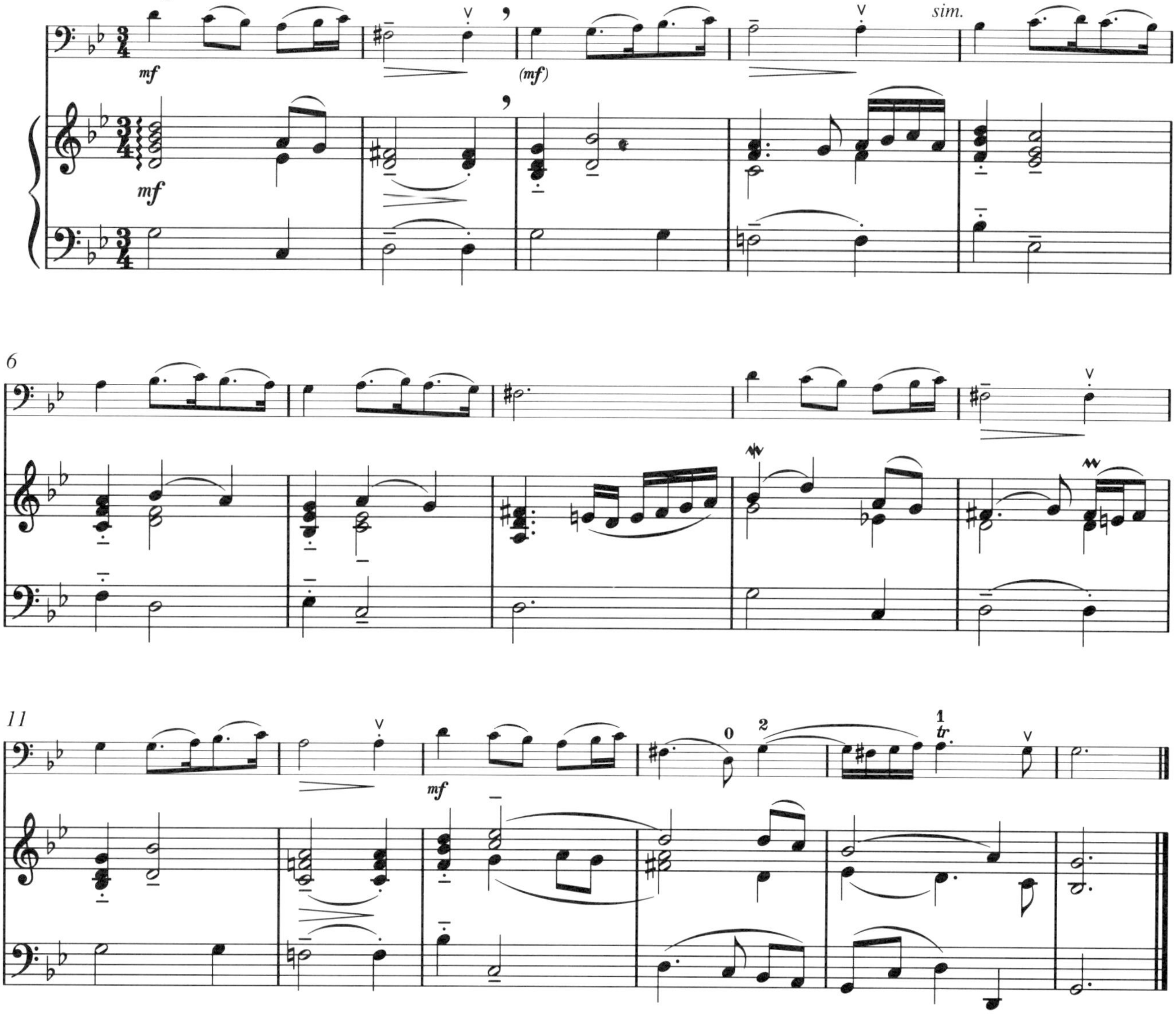

attacca Allegro (ad lib.)

Allegro

Antonio Vivaldi

Muskrat Ramble

Ray Gilbert and 'Kid' Ory

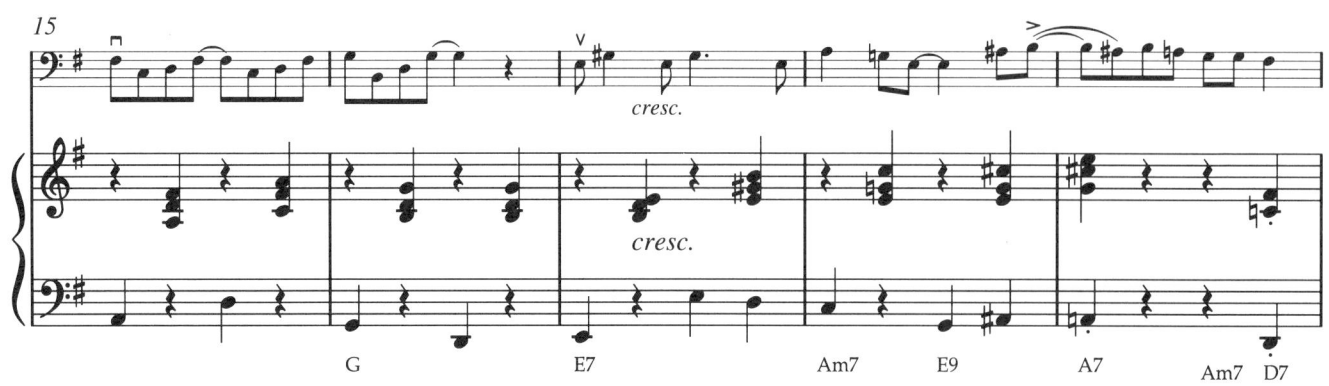

MICROJAZZ*

by Christopher Norton

MICROJAZZ is a world famous series of music for study, for teaching and especially for fun, composed by the inimitable Christopher Norton.

Collections of easy, graded pieces in various modern styles – blues, rock, jazz, rock'n'roll and so on. Designed for use with young players, but great fun for adults too!

MICROJAZZ ist eine weltberühmte Serie von Musikstücken, die vom unnachahmlichen Christopher Norton zum Studium, Unterricht und vor allem zum vergnüglichen Musizieren komponiert wurden.

Eine Sammlung einfacher, gestufter Stücke in verschiedenen modernen Stilarten wie Blues, Rock, Jazz, Rock and Roll usw. Vor allem für junge Leute gedacht, aber auch für Erwachsene ein reines Vergnügen!

MICROJAZZ, recueil de musiques: réputées mondialement, destinées à l'étude, l'enseignement, mais surtout au plaisir de les jouer! L'inimitable Christopher Norton en est l'auteur.

Collection de morceaux gradués, d'exécution facile dans divers styles modernes: blues, rock, jazz, rock'n'roll, etc… Leur conception est ciblée sur les jeunes exécutants, mais les adultes ne les dédaigneront pas non plus!

マイクロジャズは、無類の作曲家クリストファー・ノートンによる、練習のため、教授のため、そして何よりも楽しむための世界的に有名な曲集シリーズです。ブルース、ロック、ジャズ、ロックンロールなど、様々なスタイルで簡単な曲を集め、段階別に編集してあります。子供のための曲集ではありますが、大人も十分楽しむことができるでしょう!

MICROJAZZ FOR
Starters, Violin and piano *8256*
Violin and piano *7524*
Starters, Viola and piano *8257*
Viola and piano *8243*
Starters, Cello and piano *8801*
Cello and piano *7538*
Double Bass and piano *8562*
Guitar Solo *8787*, **volume 2** *9192*
Guitar Duet *8788*, **volume 2** *9193*

AND FOR FLEXIBLE ENSEMBLE – FOR 2 TO 100 PLAYERS!
Ensemble Microjazz 1 Beach Front, A Day in Majorca *8568*
Ensemble Microjazz 2 Gently Swinging, Train Blues *8569*
Ensemble Microjazz 3 Tip-Top, Metal Merchant *8570*
Ensemble Microjazz 4 In the Bag, Shoe Horn Blues *8571*
Ensemble Microjazz 1-4 on smf disk *9200*

Boosey & Hawkes Music Publishers Limited
295 Regent Street, London W1R 8JH   Ad.182

EASY REPERTOIRE FOR THE CELLO

PIECE BY PIECE 1 & 2 Sheila M. Nelson
Graded pieces in attractive contrasting styles, following on from *Right from the Start*. Includes traditional melodies, tunes from the classical repertoire and original, jazzier numbers.
Cello and Piano, Book 1 *8791*   Cello Part *8799*
Cello and Piano, Book 2 *8792*   Cello Part *8800*

PAIRS and **THREES AND FOURS** Sheila M. Nelson
Simple duets, trios and quartets written in easy keys, which are an ideal introduction to part playing.
Pairs *3927*
Threes and Fours – Score and two parts *3940*
                    Parts 1 and 3 *3941*
                    Parts 2 and 4 *3942*

TUNES YOU KNOW 1 & 2 arr. Sheila M. Nelson
16 favourite well-known tunes in easy arrangements for cello duet.
Tunes You Know 1 *8576*
Tunes You Know 2 *8577*

MY CELLO TUNES Andrew Toovey *8809*
7 easy solo pieces for the young cellist.

MICROJAZZ FOR STARTERS Christopher Norton *8801*
20 easy pieces in up-beat *Microjazz* styles for beginners.

MICROJAZZ FOR CELLO Christopher Norton *7538*
A collection of easy, graded pieces in popular styles including blues, rock, jazz and rock'n'roll. Fun for both young players and adults too!

THE JUNGLE BOOK Charles Dakin *1782*
A delightful collection of 16 pieces for two, three and four cellos featuring the characters from *The Jungle Book*.

PIECE BY PIECE 1 & 2 Sheila M. Nelson
Dieser Folgeband zu *Right from the Start* bietet wiederum neue Stücke nach Schwierigkeitsgrad sortiert. Die kontrastierenden Stilrichtungen schließen traditionelle Melodien, wie auch welche aus dem klassischen Repertoire ein. Originalkompositionen im jazzigen Stil runden den Band ab.
Violoncello und Klavier, Bd. 1 *8791*   Solostimme separat *8799*
Violoncello und Klavier, Bd. 2 *8792*   Solostimme separat *8800*

PAIRS und **THREES AND FOURS** Sheila M. Nelson
Leichte Duette, Trios und Quartette in einfachen Tonarten, die eine ideale Einführung in das Ensemblespiel bieten.
Pairs *3927*
Threes and Fours – Partitur und zwei Stimmen *3940*
                    Stimmen 1 und 3 *3941*
                    Stimmen 2 und 4 *3942*

TUNES YOU KNOW 1 & 2 bearb. von Sheila M. Nelson
16 bekannte und beliebte Melodien in leichten Bearbeitungen für 2 Violoncelli.
Tunes You Know 1 *8576*
Tunes You Know 2 *8577*

MY CELLO TUNES Andrew Toovey *8809*
7 leichte Solostücke für junge Cellisten.

MICROJAZZ FOR STARTERS Christopher Norton *8801*
20 leichte Stücke mit flotten *Microjazz*-Stilelementen für Anfänger.

MICROJAZZ FOR CELLO Christopher Norton *7538*
Eine Sammlung von leichten, nach Schwierigkeitsgrad geordneten Stücken verschiedener, populärer Stilrichtungen wie "Blues", Rock, Jazz und "Rock'n'Roll". Viel spaß – sowohl für erwachsene Spieler!

THE JUNGLE BOOK (Das Dschungelbuch) Charles Dakin *1782*
Eine hübsche Sammlung von 16 Stücken für zwei, drei und vier Violoncelli mit den Figuren aus dem *Dschungelbuch*.

PIECE BY PIECE 1 & 2 Sheila M. Nelson
Des morceaux classés par ordre de difficulté croissante dans des styles attrayants et variés, qui viennent à la suite de *Right from the Start*. Ils comprennent des mélodies traditionnelles, des extraits du répertoire classique et des pièces originales dans l'esprit du jazz.
Violoncelle et Piano, Cahier 1 *8791*   Partie de Violoncelle *8799*
Violoncelle et Piano, Cahier 2 *8792*   Partie de Violoncelle *8800*

PAIRS et **THREES AND FOURS** Sheila M. Nelson
Duos, trios et quatuors faciles dans des tonalités simples qui constituent une introduction idéale au jeu d'ensemble.
Pairs *3927*
Threes and Fours – Partition et deux parties *3940*
                    Parties 1 et 3 *3941*   Parties 2 et 4 *3942*

TUNES YOU KNOW 1 & 2 arr. Sheila M. Nelson
16 airs favoris bien connus dans des arrangements faciles pour duo de violoncelles.
Tunes You Know 1 *8576*   Tunes You Know 2 *8577*

MY CELLO TUNES Andrew Toovey *8809*
7 solos faciles pour le jeune violoncelliste.

MICROJAZZ FOR STARTERS Christopher Norton *8801*
20 morceaux faciles pour débutants dans le style entraînant des *Microjazz*.

MICROJAZZ FOR CELLO Christopher Norton *7538*
Une collection de morceaux faciles classés par ordre de difficulté croissante, dans des styles populaires tels que le blues, le rock, le jazz et le rock'n'roll. Amusement certain pour les jeunes musiciens comme pour les adultes!

THE JUNGLE BOOK Charles Dakin *1782*
Une collection ravissante de 16 morceaux pour deux, trois et quatre violoncelles inspirés par les personnages du *Livre de la Jungle*.

Boosey & Hawkes Music Publishers Limited
295 Regent Street, London W1R 8JH

Ad. 172

AMAZING SOLOS
for cello and keyboard

selected and arranged by Howard Harrison

BOOSEY & HAWKES

London · New York · Berlin · Sydney

Composer's Note

The music in this book is appealing, sometimes truly great music which just happens to be simple. None of the pieces is merely 'educational' – almost all of them had successful lives of their own before they found their way here – and they have all been chosen for their individual, purely musical strengths. However, the book is more than just a collection of performable pieces; the pieces in it are roughly graded and very varied in their demands, so that any player who works through them will have the chance to consolidate and polish their technique. They are also more than usually varied in style, so I hope they will give some unexpected pleasures and signpost some interesting and enjoyable pathways that might otherwise have remained unexplored.

Anmerkung des Komponisten

Die Stücke in diesem Band, von denen einige besonders bedeutsam sind, sind äußerst ansprechend und gleichzeitig auch einfach. Es sind keine typischen Unterrichtsstücke – die meisten waren durchaus erfolgreich, bevor sie, aufgrund ihrer individuellen, rein musikalischen Stärken in diesem Band aufgenommen wurden. Es handelt sich dabei jedoch nicht nur um eine Sammlung aufführbarer Stücke, sondern um solche, die dem Spieler aufgrund ihrer Stufungen und vielseitigen Anforderungen die Möglichkeit zum Konsolidieren und Ausfeilen ihrer Fähigkeit geben. Auch stilmäßig sind sie von besonderer Vielseitigkeit und ich hoffe, daß sie nicht nur eine Quelle der Freude, sondern auch ein Wegweiser zu neuen, bisher unerforschten Pfaden sein werden.

Note du Compositeur

Les musiques de ce recueil pour si attirantes qu'elles soient – et même parfois importantes – n'en sont pas moins d'une grande simplicité. Il n'est pas de morceau qui ne soit qu'éducationnel, presque tous ont eu une carrière réussie avant de se retrouver groupés. De plus leur choix fut dicté par leurs caractères individuels, purement musicaux. L'ensemble est toutefois bien davantage qu'une simple collection de morceaux jouables: gradués de façon approximative, ils requièrent de la part des exécutants des talents divers, tant et si bien que la technique de ceux qui les joueront tous s'en trouvera consolidée et perfectionnée. La variété de leurs styles permettra donc, du moins je l'espère, qu'ils soient source de plaisirs inattendus autant qu'indicateurs de voies intéressantes qui, sans eux, seraient restées sans explorateurs.

作曲家の言葉

　本作品集には魅力的で、時には本当に偉大な名曲でありながらも、演奏が簡単な曲ばかりを集めました。単なる「教材」は一曲もありません。ほとんど全てが、ここに選ばれる前に既に有名になった曲です。そして全て、独立した、純粋に音楽的な要素を前提に選ばれたものです。しかし、単なる曲集でもありません。各曲は大まかに段階が付けられ、それぞれ様々な要素を必要としますから、演奏することによってテクニックを磨き、確実なものとすることができるのです。また、一般の作品集よりも様々なスタイルを取り混ぜていますから、思ってもいなかった喜びを体験され、そうでなければ経験することのなかったような、面白く、楽しい道を発見する手がかりとなればと願っています。

This compilation © Copyright 1994 by Boosey & Hawkes Music Publishers Ltd.
Special thanks to Chris Dare for help with editing the cello part.
Cover design by Russell Stretten Design, London NW1 3SA
Music set by Jack Thompson.

CONTENTS · INHALT · TABLE DE MATIERES

Bliss

Franz Schubert

Woogie Boogie

Howard Harrison

Chorale
from the St. Matthew Passion

Johann Sebastian Bach

Tanz des Burgermeisters
(Mayor's Dance)

Michael Praetorius

Byker Hill

English traditional

Lovely Joan

English traditional

Scherzando
from For Children

Béla Bartók

Pleasantry II
from For Children

Béla Bartók

Allegro

Wolfgang Amadeus Mozart

This arrangement © Copyright 1994 by Boosey & Hawkes Music Publishers Ltd.

Troika
from Lieutenant Kijé

Serge Prokofieff

Lord Inchiquin

Turlough Carolan

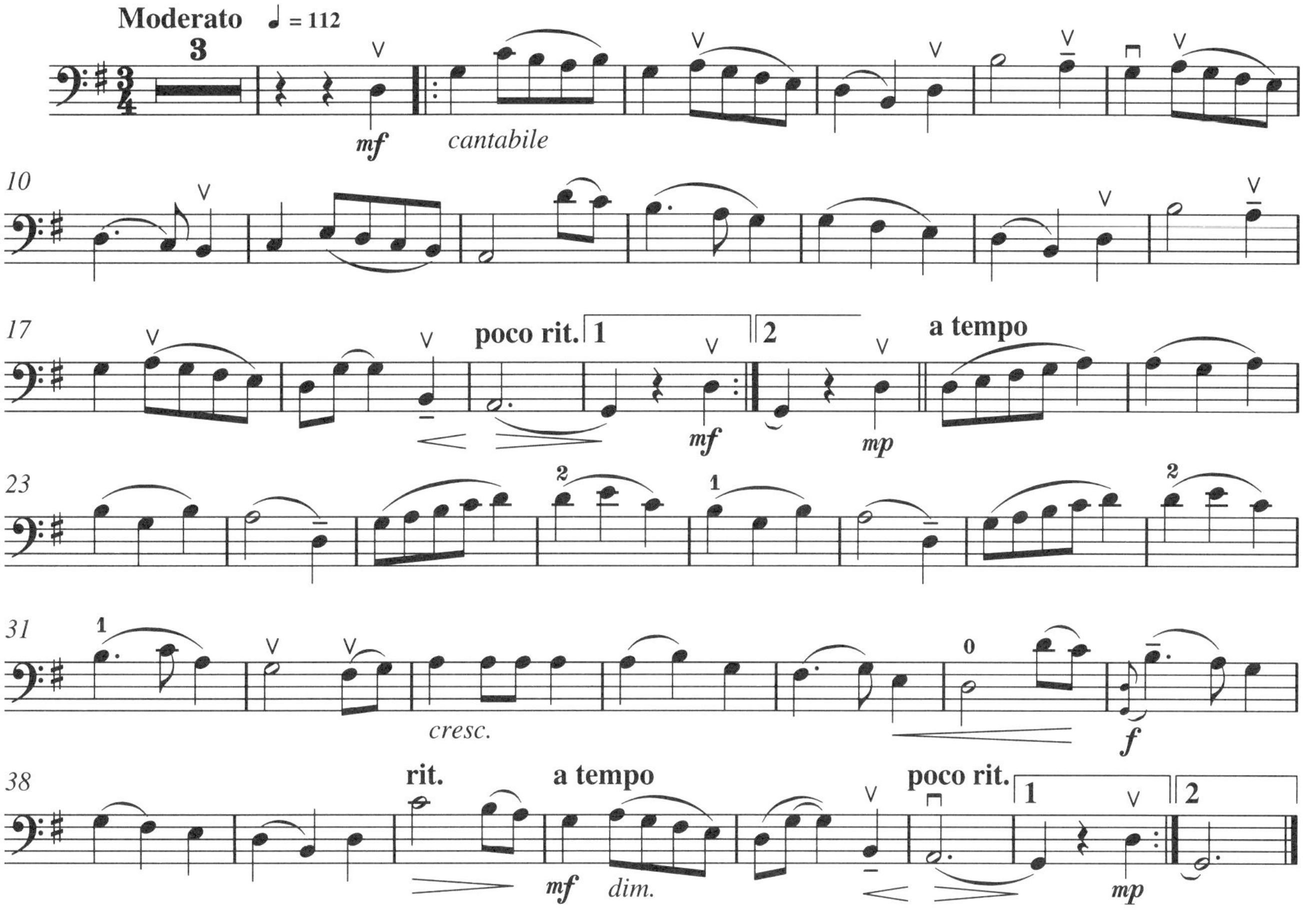
Moderato ♩ = 112
3
mf
cantabile
10
17
poco rit.
1
2
mf
mp
a tempo
23
31
cresc.
f
38
rit.
a tempo
mf
dim.
poco rit.
mp

Tambourin I

Jacques Aubert

Vivo 𝅗𝅥 = c. 90
mf
5
9
mp
13
cresc.
mf
attacca Tambourin II ad lib.

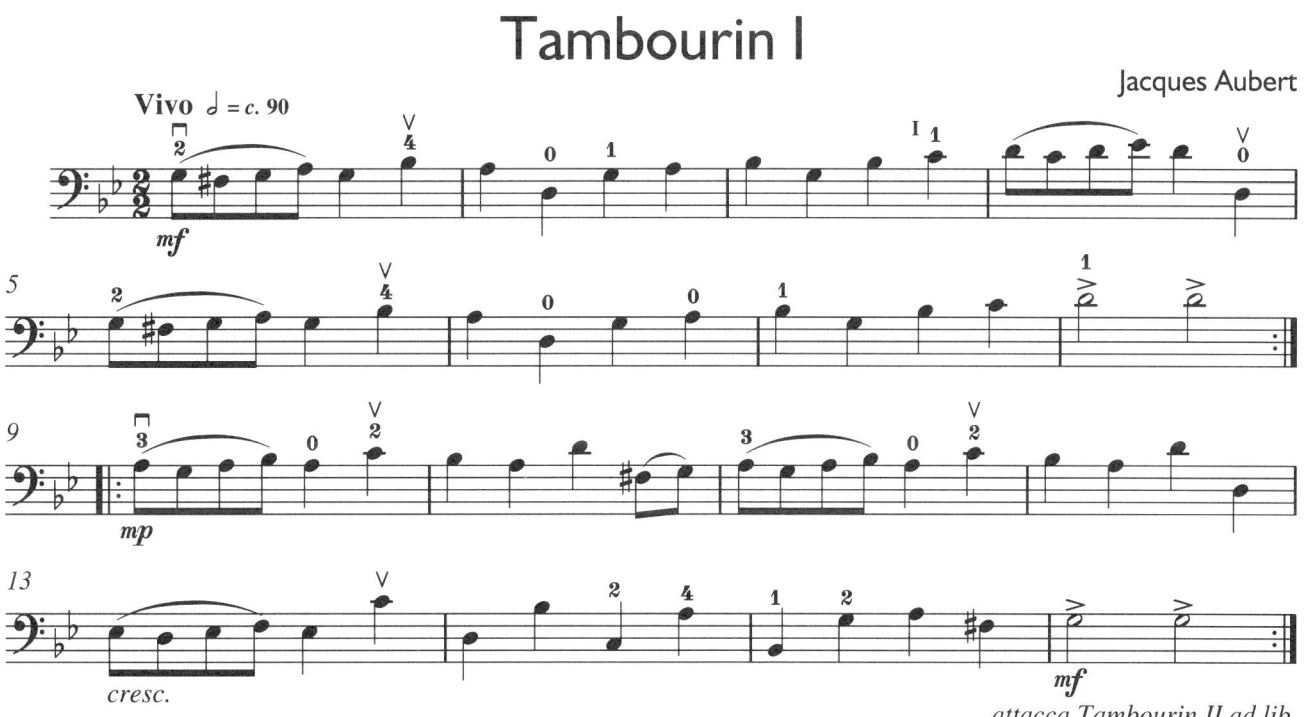

Tambourin II

Jacques Aubert

Vivo ♩ = c. 90

Mayim, Mayim

Israeli traditional

♩ = 96

("May- im")

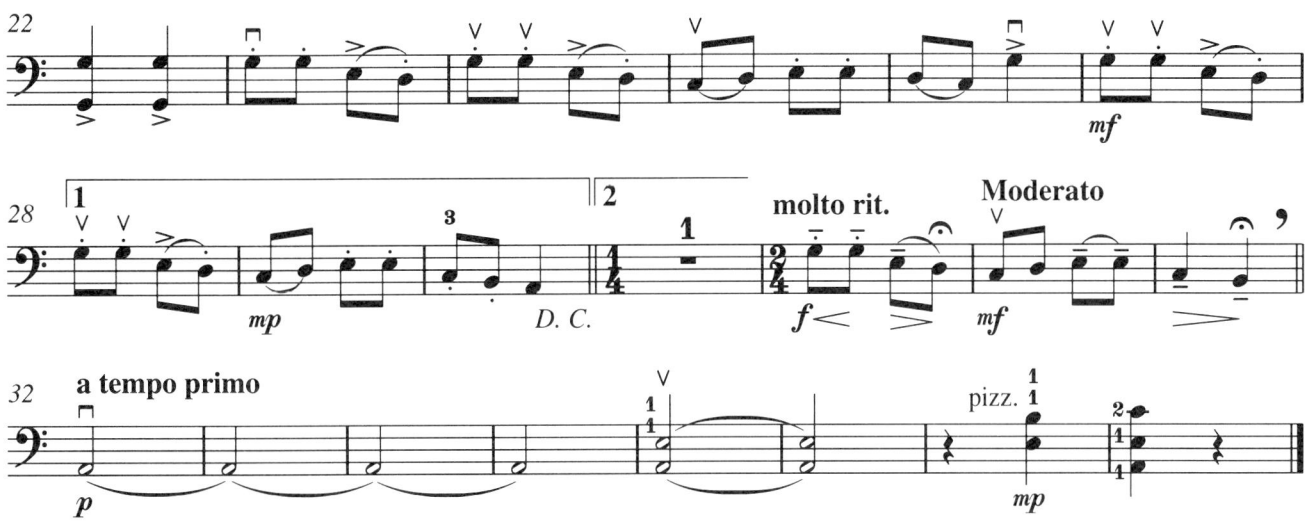

11

The House of the Rising Sun

American traditional

12

Stars, No Moon

Peruvian traditional

This arrangement © Copyright 1994 by Boosey & Hawkes Music Publishers Ltd.

Paragon Rag

Scott Joplin

This arrangement © Copyright 1994 by Boosey & Hawkes Music Publishers Ltd.

Three Moravian Folk Songs

1. Budíček
(Morning Call)

Leoš Janáček

2. Psaníčko
(Little Letter)

Leoš Janáček

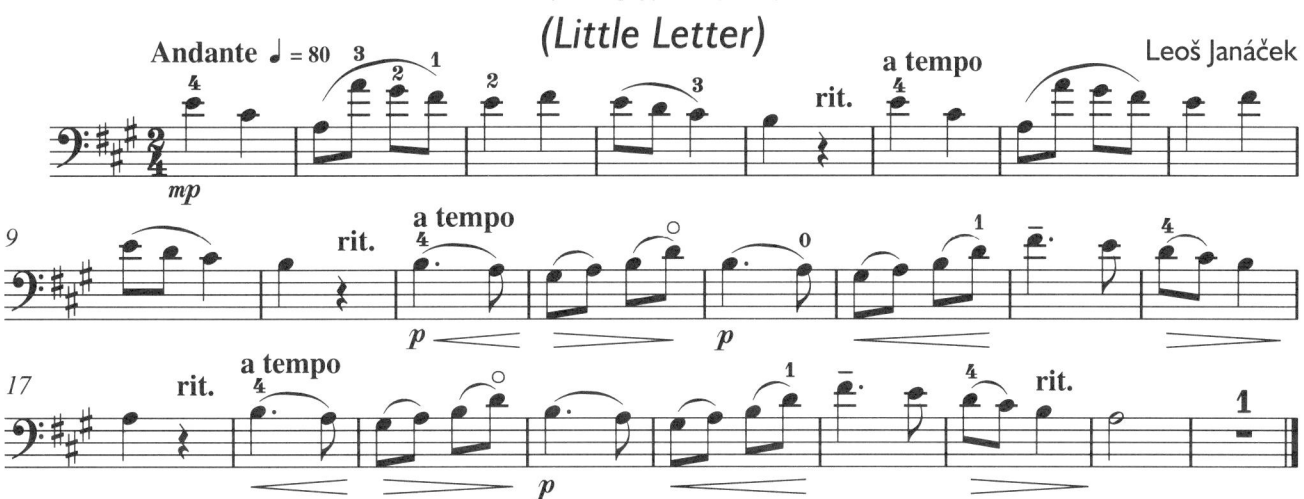

3. Stalost
(Constancy)

Leoš Janáček

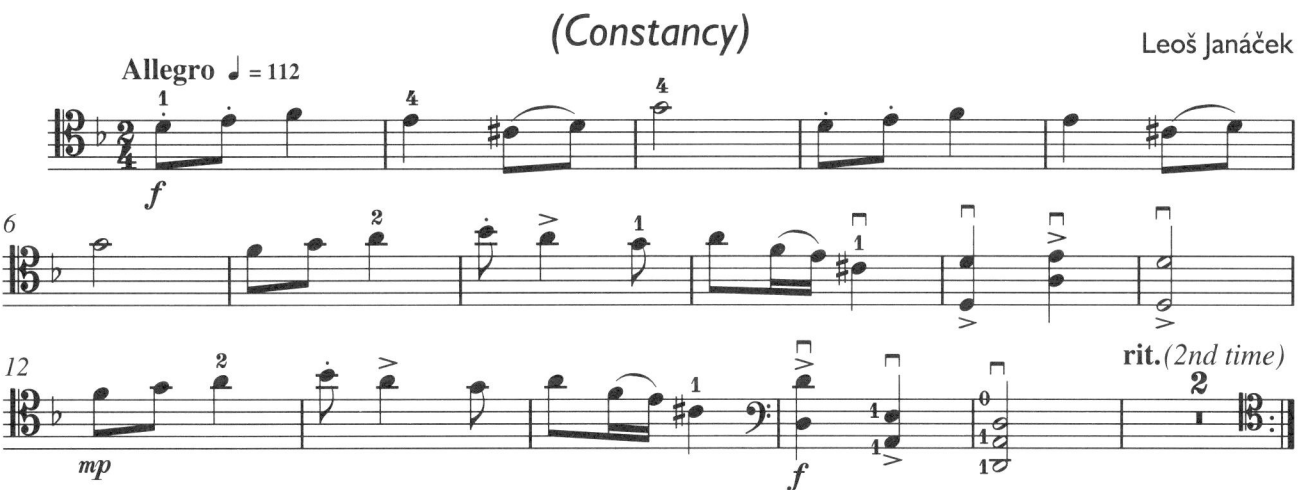

Maria
from West Side Story

Leonard Bernstein

The Blue Beyond

Howard Harrison

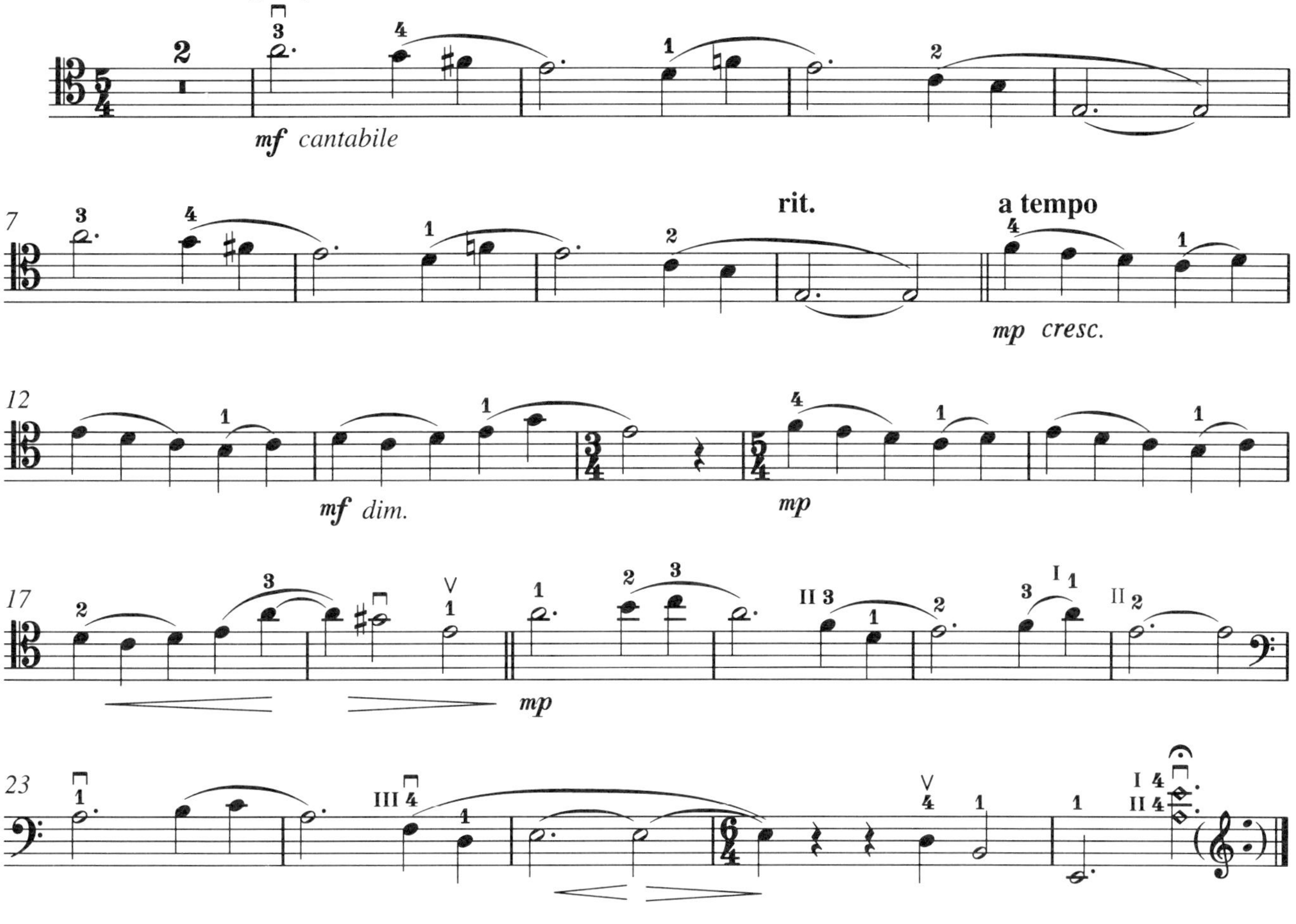

Larghetto

Antonio Vivaldi

attacca Allegro (ad lib.)

Allegro

Antonio Vivaldi

This arrangement © Copyright 1994 by Boosey & Hawkes Music Publishers Ltd.

Muskrat Ramble

Ray Gilbert and 'Kid' Ory

Reproduced and printed by
Halstan & Co. Ltd., Amersham, Bucks., England